Mishmeres HaKodesh V'HaChinuch

of the

Batei Din Tzedek of Kehillah Kedoshah Bnei Brak

POB 110, Bnei Brak • IVR 03-6768218 • Fax 03-5745504

בס"ד, אדר תשפ"ב

<u>Approbation</u>

We hereby approve the children's book
Stop on Red! Anger Ahead!
written exclusively by Ahuva Raanan.

The contents have been reviewed
and found suitable for *yerei Shamayim*.
The author has merited *siyata diShemaya*,
publishing many children's books that promote values
important for raising Jewish children with good *middos*.

May we merit the blessing that
"we and our children know Your Torah."
אמן כן יהי רצון

Rabbi Mordechai Blau

Originally published in Hebrew as *Atzor ad Shehaka'as Ya'avor!*

ISBN 978-1-68025-193-7

FELDHEIM PUBLISHERS
POB 34549
Jerusalem, Israel

208 Airport Executive Park
Nanuet, NY 10954

Illustrated by Sofi Agres
Translated by Aviva Rappaport
Proofread by Cindy Scarr
Graphic Design by Ettie Shmidov

www.feldheim.com

Ahuva Raanan

STOP ON RED! ANGER AHEAD!

Translated by Aviva Rappaport
Illustrated by Sofi Agres

My Toolbox Books
For the development of emotion regulation in early childhood

When Yossi was a baby,
he didn't even know Angry-Mad.
But a few years later,
when Yossi got bigger,
he got to know him very well.

Sometimes, Angry-Mad is sleeping.
He's quiet, and he doesn't move.

Until...

Something annoying happens.
Then Angry-Mad wakes up, irritated.

Once, when Yossi was three,
he was at the playground.
He saw a boy swinging on the only swing,
going up and down, up and down.

Yossi wanted to swing too,
and he didn't want to wait.
He wanted the boy to get off
right away.

But the boy just kept swinging
and didn't get off!

Yossi grabbed the swing
and shook it hard.
The boy got scared
and almost cried.

Yossi's mother saw what was happening.
She came right over to calm down
the boy on the swing.

To Yossi, she said firmly,
"I see you want to swing
but I don't allow any pushing."

Yossi got very annoyed,
and Angry-Mad inside him
woke up right away and made
a big fuss. Yossi cried
and shouted and got mad
and didn't listen to his mother
AT ALL.

The boy kept swinging on the swing
even though he knew Yossi wanted a turn.
This made Angry-Mad **furious**.
Angry-Mad got bigger and bigger
and told Yossi to push the boy very hard.

Yossi pushed the boy very hard
and then...
The boy fell off the swing
and got a big bang.
It hurt a lot and
he cried.

Mommy was very upset.
"That's enough for today," she said.
"We're going home right now!"
She wanted to calm down that terrible
Angry-Mad.

It happened again, this time at dinner.
Yossi was very hungry and waiting for his soup.
But Chedvah got hers first!

Angry-Mad woke up and quickly got very big...

Splash!

Yossi got angry and pushed the bowl.
The soup spilled all over
and made the kitchen all dirty.

One day, Yossi saw that his new toy
wasn't in its usual place.
It also looked a little scratched.
Yossi knew why!
His brother Rafael must have taken it
without permission!

Angry-Mad started to get
bigger and bigger...

Yossi got mad at Rafael
and hit him hard and it
really hurt Rafael.

A different time, in the afternoon,
Yossi built a zoo. All of a sudden,
Chedvah walked by and accidentally
knocked over the fence.

Angry-Mad went wild
and told Yossi to hit her!

And that's what happened again and again.
Every time someone bothered Yossi
or spoiled his fun, Angry-Mad got bigger and bigger.

He puffed up until he almost burst,
and because of him,
Yossi exploded in anger
and yelled wildly
and then he felt very,
very sorry about it.

Abba and Mommy were very unhappy
each time it happened.
They said to Yossi,
"You have to stop Angry-Mad in time
and make sure he doesn't
get bigger!"

But nothing changed...
Every time things didn't go
the way Yossi wanted,
Yossi got upset and angry
and spoiled everyone's fun.

One day, Yossi was riding in the car
with his father. Abba was in a big rush,
but whenever he saw a red light,
he made sure to stop in time.

Once when they were stopped
at a red light Abba said to Yossi,
"It's a good thing there are
traffic lights. They prevent
accidents even when people
are in a rush!"

All of a sudden,
Yossi had an idea.
"I'll build an imaginary
traffic light in my mind,
with a bright red light,
and I'll turn it on
every time Angry-Mad
starts to wake up!"

When Ima heard Yossi's great idea
she got very excited and added a few steps:

"**STOP** on red.
"**RELAX** on yellow.
"**SOLVE** on green."

Now, every time Angry-Mad wakes up,
the red light of Yossi's traffic light goes on
and gives him a strong signal inside.
Then Yossi tells himself,
"STOP on red! Anger ahead!"

That's how, thanks to the red light, Yossi stops.
Then he turns on the yellow light and starts to relax
and let go of the anger he feels.

How?

Sometimes he washes his face.
Sometimes he drinks a glass of water.
Sometimes he sits down to color,
or goes outside to ride his bike.

When Yossi feels calm and relaxed,
it's time for the next step.
Now he turns on the green traffic light.

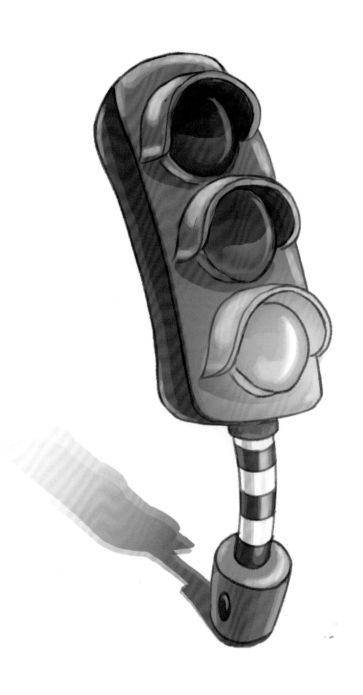

When the green light goes on,
Yossi talks about what happened
and tries to solve the problem.

Maybe we can take turns!

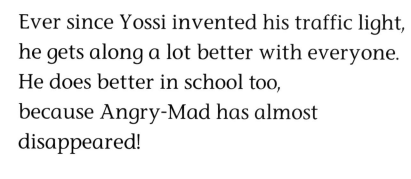

Ever since Yossi invented his traffic light,
he gets along a lot better with everyone.
He does better in school too,
because Angry-Mad has almost
disappeared!

Every time Angry-Mad starts to wake up,
Yossi says to him and also to himself,
"Wait a second! You need to **STOP on red.
Anger ahead**!"

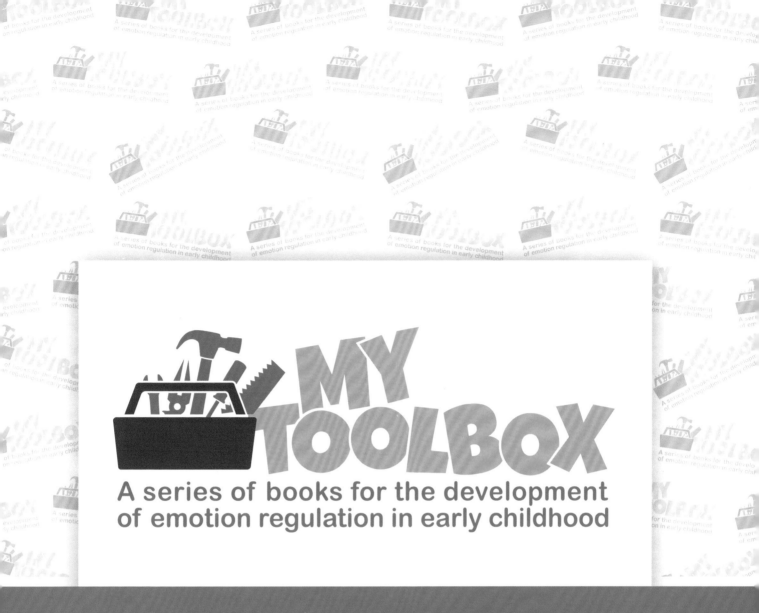

MY TOOLBOX

A series of books for the development
of emotion regulation in early childhood

For parents, words to the wise.
And for children, a happy surprise!

Ways to cope and to inspire hope

My Toolbox Books
For the development of emotion regulation in early childhood

Emotion regulation

Emotion regulation, also called emotional regulation or self-regulation, is the process by which we manage and control our emotions. The goal is a balance between two opposite ways of dealing with emotions: denying their existence or allowing them unbridled release.

With emotion regulation, we express feelings. We don't suppress or deny them. But neither do we allow them uncontrolled release.

Using emotion regulation, we learn how to control our emotions and the way we express them by first learning to identify the emotion and understand it.

The importance of emotion regulation

A child's ability to regulate his emotions has a major impact on his healthy psychological development. Successful emotion regulation leads to emotional health and balance.

An emotionally balanced child can adapt to new situations and form relationships more easily. He can more readily overcome stressful situations and deal with pain or difficult emotions. Emotion regulation skills affect communication, social skills, self-image—actually, all areas of personal and interpersonal behavior.

Children who have difficulty regulating their emotions are less available for learning tasks and may be less well-liked by their peers. In contrast, children who use cognitive methods to control their emotions and behavior do well in school, have good social skills, and are accepted and well-liked by their peers.

The role of parents in a child's development of emotion regulation

A child's ability to regulate his emotions develops through his interactions with the significant figures in his life. The determining factor is how his parents react to his distress signals, his behavior, and the way he expresses his feelings.

From infancy, a child learns to organize and regulate his responses to stimuli he perceives from within (such as hunger or discomfort), and from without (such as sights, sounds, touch, and movement) with the help of his parents. He draws comfort from contact with them when they pick him up, hold him, feed him, and rock him until he calms down.

As the child grows, the parents' ways of calming him expand to include other options. They may comfort him through hugging and kissing, encourage him with reassuring words, or offer him different ways of dealing with his negative feelings. Such interactions bring children to gradually internalize the role of relaxation, and they learn to calm themselves in different ways.

Parental modeling of emotion regulation also plays a significant role, as the child observes and absorbs the way his parents respond to their own emotional states.

Ways to promote emotion regulation in young children

Recognize when your child is struggling with an emotion

The first stage in helping your child develop the ability to regulate his emotions is to create a safe emotional space for him. It's a place where you see things from your child's point of view and accept his thoughts and feelings without judging or criticizing them.

Ignoring or dismissing a child's feelings won't make them go away; it just makes the child feel that no one understands him, that there's no way to cope with such feelings, and that it's best to hide such feelings from the people closest to him.

But when parents create a safe emotional space for their child's feelings and issues, they help him learn how to control his emotions and cope with challenges.

Help your child identify and name the feeling

Words play an important role in the development of emotion regulation. Without words, it's impossible to identify an emotion, and therefore it can't be regulated. For a child to be able to regulate his emotions, he must recognize them, distinguish one from another, and name them.

Guiding the child to become aware of what he is feeling begins with spontaneous statements by parents as they identify the child's emotion and reflect it back to him. For example: "You're so happy right now!" Or, "You're tired and don't have any patience."

The more parents use emotion words to share their feelings, the more they help their child understand his own feelings and know how to express them.

Suggest ways to express emotion

Parents can help their child learn to regulate his emotions by teaching him legitimate ways to express his feelings. The goal is to acknowledge the feeling while encouraging him to control it.

Distressful or negative emotions can be regulated using various strategies:

1. Strategies based on contact with others. For example: sharing, asking for help.
2. Action-based strategies. For example: running, drinking, jumping rope, taking deep breaths, muscle relaxation.
3. Strategies based on mastery of thought processes. For example: distraction, delaying the response, reframing, and reassuring internal speech.

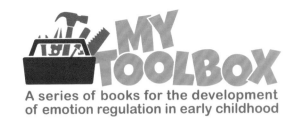

A series of books for the development of emotion regulation in early childhood

The My Toolbox series helps develop emotion regulation in early childhood

The My Toolbox series is designed to help young children develop emotion regulation skills. Each book in the series spotlights a specific, commonly experienced emotion. Rich illustrations and language bring to life various incidents that trigger the emotion. Feelings are named and described, giving the child the vocabulary to help him express his own feelings.

Each book also offers targeted strategies to help regulate the emotion:

♥ Through **identification with the protagonist** and his challenges, the child learns to recognize, name, and regulate his feelings just like the hero of the story.

♥ The rhyme taught in each book guides the child to achieve regulation by **changing his thoughts** and controlling them.

♥ The tool offered in each book lets the child adapt for his own use an **action or physical technique** that will help him manage and regulate the emotion.

Regulating the emotion of feeling anger

**"One who breaks utensils in anger…
is like one who serves idols."**

(Shabbos 105b)

**"המשבר כליו בחמתו…
יהא בעיניך כעובד עובדה זרה."**

(מסכת שבת דף ק"ה ע"ב)

Anger is an emotion that is an integral part of life. The problems associated with anger have to do with how anger is expressed or managed.

Every emotion serves a function. When we use our emotions correctly, they help us succeed in life.

Like other unpleasant emotions, anger is a basic, natural, and legitimate emotion that serves a purpose. Anger acts as a warning signal, telling us that something is wrong in our environment and that we must act to change it. In other words: anger helps us defend ourselves against various threats or harm. It also helps us learn and internalize important values and social norms, such as: telling the truth, not taking something that doesn't belong to us, being considerate of others, etc. When people are angry at us, it tells us we've crossed a boundary.

Anger can also help us protect ourselves. For instance, if someone crosses one of our boundaries, our anger signals that we are unwilling to accept this behavior.

Anger has a lot of energy that when managed effectively can help us repair and build. However, when we find it hard to contain the anger, and it flares up, we may behave in harmful or ineffective ways that can provoke aggression or rejection toward us and create a cascade of unpleasant and unproductive emotions and behaviors. Often, after we calm down, we regret our angry reaction or are unhappy with the consequences.

Practicing self-control
"The entire world exists only in the merit of the person who restrains his words at the time of a quarrel"

(Chullin 89a)

Researchers of brain activity have shown that emotions are generated by communication between different parts of the brain. One of the key parts of the process is the thalamus, which relays motor and sensory signals to the cerebral cortex, the thinking part of the brain, which makes the information meaningful to us.

However, not all information passes from the thalamus directly to this thinking part of the brain. A small amount of it goes directly to the amygdala, the area responsible for emotions. The amygdala reads and responds to stimuli faster but much less accurately than the cerebral cortex, and so may trigger an emotional response before our thought processes have figured out what our best response would be.

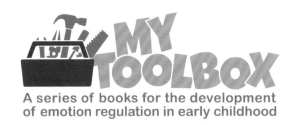

To protect us from danger and harm in situations of intense emotion, the information passed to the amygdala activates a series of nerves that stream hormones into the blood, which cause the body to be alert and produce automatic defensive mechanisms (fight or flight). For example, if we hear a sudden loud noise, our body will respond automatically by changing our breathing, heart rate, blinking, and so on. If someone gets angry and yells at us, an automatic response would most likely be aggressive and possibly even violent.

The instinctive survival mechanism is there to protect us. It offers a quick, automatic response when even a slight delay could be dangerous. However, in many instances, our initial automatic response doesn't serve us well in everyday life.

Self-control is the ability to respond to people, events, or situations after careful consideration and not out of an automatic survival response such as escape, violence, or self-blame. A person with self-control can regulate his emotions and choose the appropriate behavior when he encounters a problematic situation. He can control the intensity of his reaction and the way he expresses himself.

Self-control has been shown to be important for success in all areas of life. People with self-control are people with heightened self-awareness and well-developed interpersonal skills. They are healthy, balanced, and successful at dealing with life's challenges.

Self-control is a skill that develops gradually during the developmental process and is acquired primarily through training and experience.

The traffic light as a tool for developing self-control

Step 1: STOP

When you want to teach children self-control skills, the first step they must learn is to stop.

This stops the automatic survival response triggered before the information reaches the higher parts of the brain.

Many times when a child is upset, he needs a calm, emotionally regulated adult to authoritatively, calmly, and supportively help him stop any wild or hurtful behavior. As the child repeatedly practices stopping, he gets better and better at it and becomes empowered.

The stop made at this stage—whether done independently by the child after cognitive training or with the help of an adult—allows information to reach the higher parts of the brain and stops the fight-or-flight responses that stem from feeling threatened.

Step 2: RELAX

The second step in acquiring the skill of self-control is finding ways to calm down.

This step allows the child to transition from an agitated state to a calm state. Below you will find various ideas that can help someone moderate anger and calm down. Some of these ideas are designed to calm the body through relaxation, deep breathing, or exercise. Others are intended to distract the person from the upsetting issue.

Relaxation and deep-breathing skills need to be learned and practiced before they can be used. The relaxation and deep-breathing techniques that appear below may be helpful.

Before moving on to the next step, make sure the child is calm and completely relaxed and open to talking about the problem in a positive and creative frame of mind.

Step 3: SOLVE

Once the child has calmed down, it is important to help them solve the problem that triggered their anger.

1. State the problem from the child's perspective: *"You really wanted to get it first."*
2. State the problem from the perspective of the environment: *"But today it wasn't your turn to get it."* Or, *"Today, I decided to let so-and-so be first."*
3. Suggest different possible ways to solve the problem.
4. Choose one of the solutions.

If the child has already exploded in anger or hit someone, the conversation (after the child is thoroughly calm and relaxed, of course) can be based on the following questions:

1. *What happened?*
2. *What was the problem?*
3. *What can be done so this doesn't happen again?*

To help the child internalize this strategy, pay attention to even small steps that show an improvement in his ability to control and stop—and praise him for them. Guide, encourage, and support the child through the process. Praise specific behavior that demonstrates self-control, describing each positive action taken by the child: "When Yossi sat down in your seat, instead of pushing him or hitting him, you said to him, using words, 'This is my seat.' That was great!"

Play
with toys you like

Drink
something hot

1-2-3-4-5-6-7-8-9-10
Count
slowly from 1 to 10

Listen
to relaxing music

MY TOOLBOX
A series of books for the development of emotion regulation in early childhood

What do you do when you're angry?

Ten ideas
to help you
calm down

Drink
cold water

Go outside
to the fresh air

Wash
your face

Think
about something
pleasant

Take
three deep breaths

Relax and release
the tension

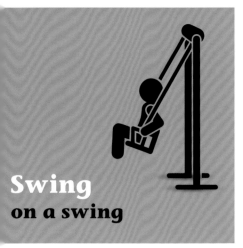

Swing
on a swing

Run
around the table
for one minute

Jump
up and down
ten times

Break the ice
in a frozen bottle
of water

MY TOOLBOX
A series of books for the development
of emotion regulation in early childhood

What do you do when you're angry?

Ten ideas
to help you
release
the anger

Do exercises
and gymnastics

Kick
a tree trunk

Punch
a pillow

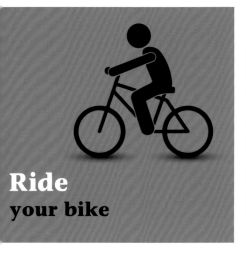

Ride
your bike

Scribble hard
on a piece of paper

Shout
into a pillow

Deep Breathing

One of the things that can help us calm down and release tension is deep breathing. When we're tense and angry, our breathing is shallow and fast. When we slow down and take a deep breath, we bring fresh, clean air into our body. This helps calm anger, tension, and anxiety.

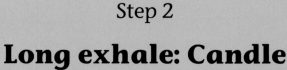
Flower-Candle Breath

Use your imagination to help you take deep breaths.

Step 1	Step 2
Deep breath: Flower	**Long exhale: Candle**
Pretend you're smelling a flower and slowly take fresh, clean air into your body.	Pretend you're trying to blow out a candle and slowly blow out the air in your lungs.

© My Toolbox

Practice these two steps until you feel like you know how to take a deep breath.

**When you want to calm down, pay attention to the way you're breathing.
Take three deep breaths! It will help you!**

Relaxation

One way to help us relax and release tension is to relax our bodies.
When we're tense and angry, our body is tense and tight.
It's sort of like uncooked spaghetti.
When we're relaxed and comfortable,
our body is relaxed and comfortable,
sort of like cooked spaghetti.

Tense body

Uncooked spaghetti

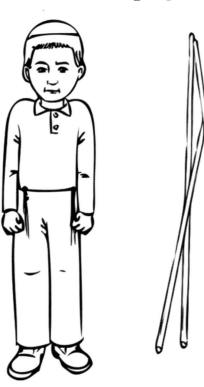

Relaxed body

Cooked spaghetti

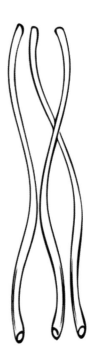

When you want to relax, pay attention to your body. It will help you!

Tighten to Relax

(Dr. Edmund Jacobson)

One highly effective relaxation technique is to tense and relax all your muscles one by one. Chose a muscle in your body, squeeze it tightly for five seconds (5 seconds), and then release it. (Make sure not to hold your breath when you're tensing a muscle.)

Relax your body

Feet
Lift your feet.
Slowly count to five and...lower your feet!

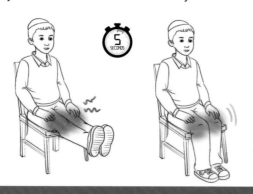

Stomach
Pull in your stomach.
Slowly count to five, and... let go!

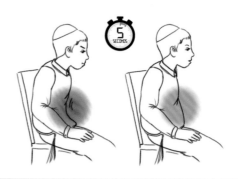

Arms
Bend your arms and clench your fists to tighten the muscles. Slowly count to five, and...let go!

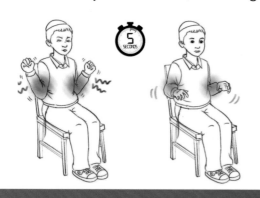

Hands
Make a fist and squeeze it tight.
Slowly count to five, and...let go!

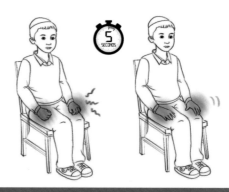

Relax your neck

Shoulders

Lift your shoulders up toward your ears. Squeeze tightly. Slowly count to five and...lower your shoulders!

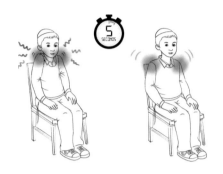

Neck

Bend your head down. Slowly count to five, and...lift it!
Turn your head to the right. Slowly count to five, and...turn it to face forward!
Turn your head to the left. Slowly count to five, and...turn it to face forward!

Relax your face

Eyes

Squeeze your eyes shut tight.
Slowly count to five and...open them!

Eyebrows

Squeeze your eyebrows.
Slowly count to five and...release them!

Forehead

Lift your eyebrows as high as you can.
Slowly count to five and...release them!

Lips

Make the biggest smile you can.
Slowly count to five, and...let go!

A traffic light that helps you stop

Here is a reminder card to help you remember the trick you learned in this book. The card teaches you the three steps you can do when you feel the anger inside you starting to grow. These three steps will help you control the anger and stop it!

Here's the new rhyme you learned in this book.
You can put it anywhere you want to help you feel better.

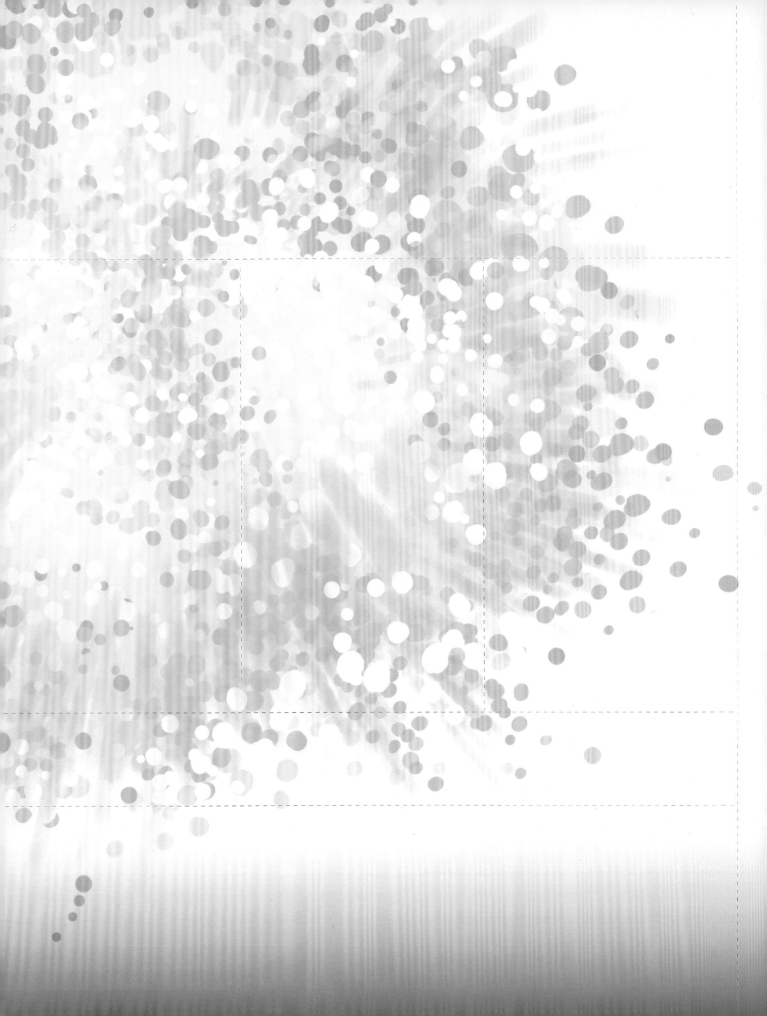